From The Movie

Disney

ENCANTO

The ULTIMATE Colouring Book

Inside this bumper colouring book, you will find lots of different and exciting ways to colour the characters from *Encanto*.

❀ **Copy Colouring** – use the small image at the top of the page to complete the picture.

❀ **Part Colouring** – complete the picture using the part-coloured backgrounds to inspire you.

❀ **Posters** – colour the amazing scenes and, with the help of an adult, cut out the pages and stick them to your bedroom wall.

AUTUMN PUBLISHING

MIRABEL

ANTONIO

JULIETA

LUISA

ISABELA

PEPA

ABUELA

BRUNO

DOLORES

AGUSTÍN

CAMILO

FELIX

Antonio's special power is that he can talk to animals.
Draw a picture of you using your own power!

Isabela creates beautiful flowers with her power! Draw a magical garden below filled with jungle plants and blooms.

Luisa is the strongest girl in Encanto.
Draw her lifting up all kinds of objects!

Camilo can transform his appearance into anything he likes.
Draw lots of versions of yourself as different creatures!

casita is a magical transforming house.
Draw your own house below.

Family is everything to the Madrigals.
Draw a picture of your family here!

GROUP CHAT